Teen.com
Book of
Poetry

Volume 1

poems of love, family,
friendship and life
written from the heart
by teens around the world

Missy Rekos, editor
editor@teen.com
Linda Beneke, assistant editor

www.teen.com

Teen.com Book of Poetry, Volume 1
Copyright © 2000

Teen.com
editor@teen.com

ISBN 0-9673540-0-5
Printed in U.S.A.

Letter From the Editor

I often have been asked to describe what Teen.com is all about and how we differ from other teen-oriented sites. This has been a blessing since it has allowed me to give much thought into who we are, where we are going, and what we want to be when we grow up. I believe Teen.com is unique for many reasons, most especially because our visitors feel that we let me be me.

We don't tell them who they are, we ask. We don't try to fit them all into one mold that we feel is a typical teenager, we provide content that is diverse. Today's teens are so bombarded with information that the term "typical teenager" is often an oxymoron. They have so much to choose from when deciding the things that make them who they are. They want to be accepted, but accepted as being unique and valuable. We want to empower our visitors to know that they can be a part of this site. They can help to create special interest areas and discussions, and share their thoughts and feelings with teens from all over the world.

I like to use the example of the comfy T-shirt. We all may dress up, we may try different looks, but in the end we put on the comfy T-shirt that feels like home. That's what Teen.com is. We are comfortable, familiar, and home. We seek to include everyone, foster differences of opinion and show the beauty of diversity. We want to be the first place teens go when they need anything from the Internet. Whether they are looking for entertainment information, homework help, fitness ideas, beauty tips or just to discuss issues with other teens, they can come to Teen.com.

I believe that we can provide the ultimate in teen-oriented information and community atmosphere in a responsible, yet fun way, and hopefully we will never really grow up.

Missy Rekos
Editor-in-Chief, Teen.com
editor@teen.com

Teen.com has become one of the most popular online teen destinations thanks to all of the people behind the screens who make it happen every day. I would like to thank the many contributors to the design, selection and production of this, our first Teen.com Book of Poetry, especially Missy Rekos, Jo-Anne Poirier, Linda Beneke, Gene Bellotti, Tina McCarthy, Geddes Munson, Lindsay Earnest, and Jennifer Stolulonis, the team who brought this book to life. As you read these poems, remember that behind each poem is a teenager that needs to be heard. Take the time to listen. Their words give us a glimpse into our future.

Gerald J. Croteau, Jr.
CEO, Teen.com
Acton, MA
February 2000

Contents

Chapter 1:

This Is Me

Voyage of the Lonely Vessel

Footsteps on the grassy dew
The sun is out, the sky is new
I trace the path of trodden grass
Back to the water, streaked like glass.

Away from ripples in the calm
The distant sands tucked in my palm
My back against the setting sun
The cool breeze through my hair will run.

I hear the rocking of my boat
Bang on the bleak and dismal moat
The once used vessel for my head
Sinks slowly to the water's bed.

The gaping puncture leaks and fills
The mirrored water slowly spills
Into the portal of the hull
Farewell split craft, now water dull.

Limbs of the shade tree block the rays
The branch, just wind struck, slowly sways
Bitter stillness pollutes the air
I look around; there's no one there.

(cont.)

Footprints fade as the dew dries
Heated drops make cloudy skies.
I feel the cool specks strike my face
Waves now crash through once stilled space.

I leave the water and the shore
Departing from the grassy floor.
Out of my dreams and out of thought
Removed from world of which I sought.

Back to life of pointless substance
No more dew drops on the grass.
Vessel for the mind has sunken
Sands of time have slowly shrunken.

Forced away from fading folly
Dreams are for the melancholy
Sunken footprints in the sand
The mental vessel's crash unplanned.

John Hagan, Ohio, U.S.A.
Age 16

The Name Upon the Stone

As we walk the narrow pathway,
From this world and to the next,
We wonder if anyone will mourn
The passing of our death.
And what mark do we leave
Upon this heartless earth?
For if we look down on our life
What is it really worth?
How long will it take
For us to be unknown?
Our name to be a mystery
To those we had once known.
And will we watch from
Shadows on the breeze,
As the world slowly destroys itself
And falls down on it's knees?
Will our spirit flit
From this world to the next?
Or will we simply become
A crumbling heap of bone?
And will we just become
The name upon the stone?

Rachel von Simson, London, England
Age 15

Mask

Everyday I wear a mask
To cover up the fear.
To hide the insecurities
Which are unwelcome here.
I want them all to be fooled
I hope no one can see,
This mask I put on to hide
My personality.
Once I tried to take it off
To show what I hid inside.
But it seemed no one understood
And much preferred the lies.

Amanda Rahn, Michigan, U.S.A.
Age 14

Still Standing

I vow,
here and now,
to never act like a ditz,
or be perceived as one.
To never try to be anyone besides myself.
To never attempt to hide my own beauty,
or make my face prettier.
I won't be conceited or hollow or shameless,
I won't tell myself I'm better than anyone,
because I'm not.
I'll never succumb to the pressures of adolescence,
or be forced into anything.
I will never let anyone tell me my dreams are impossible
or unreal or egotistical.
I don't have to hear what I don't want to.
I won't strive for popularity,
or follow in anyone else's footsteps.
I will never use my body as a weapon,
or be closed minded about anything.
If I let new experiences in,
I can accept and try to understand.
I won't be a fake,
or try and lightly talk my way out of aggravating situations.
I can take it. I am strong.
I am important. I am me.
That is why I'm still standing.

Sara Beth Cowan, Massachusetts, U.S.A.
Age 16

On the Outside Looking In...

As I look out the window,
I see long, glistening icicles framing the perfect picture,
Little pelts of snow drifting to the glittery ground,
Trees clothed in rich white blankets,
And children in fairy dust
scattering their magic on others,
While couples ride on sleigh horses.
Carols fill the air and only add to the magnificence,
Lights being hung and families bonding together,
My smile fades when I realize
I'm only on the outside looking in.

Becky Ho, California, U.S.A.
Age 14

The Life of an Abused Teenager

My body is sweaty.
Nervous,
In fear of your anger.
I walk,
Down the hall.
I hear,
You screaming.
The door squeaks,
As it opens.
There you are,
With your mad face.
Now,
You take it out on me.
You,
Slash and punch at me.
I didn't do it,
But you do not care.
Then,
One day I ran away.
Away from your anger,
And up the golden stairways of heaven.

Cara Louis , Kentucky, U.S.A.
Age 13

Trapped

I am all alone with nowhere to go
And nowhere to hide.
I am in a crowd of people,
Yet there is no one to stand by my side.
I live in two worlds, one real
And one just a dream.
I cry out for help
But I still remain unseen.
I get names thrown at me
Like a spear from a hand.
They start to bottle up inside me
Like grains of sand.
I'm strong on the outside
But my insides are tearing apart,
The pain will always be there
breaking my heart.

Elizabeth Leversha, Victoria, Australia
Age 14

Weeping Willow

The aroma still lingers
the whispers still heard,
All the pain and sorrow
Of the unspoken words.
A puddle of tears
Next to a damp soggy pillow,
In the room with the view
Of the sad weeping willow.
A girl once sat there
And cried every night,
But she fooled everyone
With her smile so bright.
Her beauty, her talent,
Her voice and her pride,
Her pain and her sorrow
She HAD to hide.
The need to be loved
Was all that she had,
And who loved a crier?
Someone always sad?
All her pain and anger
Locked deep inside,
It became to much to handle,
Emptiness where her soul should reside.

(cont.)

A decision came to her
On one dark night,
It wasn't what she wanted,
She knew it wasn't right.
Below the weeping willow
Outside of the room,
A chill passes by
And lands on her tomb.
Many tears have been cried,
Many lives changed forever,
But what's done is done
And it changes, never.
Her room remains the same,
Parents way of remembering their child,
The blankets untouched,
The clothes still piled.
Tear stains on the floor
Next to the pillow,
In the room with the view
Of the sad weeping willow.

Angie Fulton, Illinois, U.S.A.

I Am Like

I am like stars, pretty from afar and amazing and
beautiful close up.
I am like a still life picture, mysterious and colorful,
worth a thousand words.
I am like a book, an interesting cover but nothing
without the story.
I am like wallpaper, neat in a roll but beautiful
when spread across a room.
I am like a pair of jeans, nothing without the seam.
I am like china, fragile and breakable,
to be handled gently.
I am like a fireplace when lit, warm and glowing.

Jessica Burton, Kentucky, U.S.A.
Age 15

Uncertain Future

Looking into the future, and most uncertainly, too.
I see goals that will fail and dreams that will come true.
Leaps and bounds,
Ups and downs,
Challenges and pressures,
And well deserved pleasures.
But despite all this, looking into each day
And seeing the path that lays in my way,
I face it head on and put on a smile
For I know that any hardships will only last awhile.
Because dreams are the stuff that life is made of
And love is the stuff that dreams are made of.

Brittany Savory, California, U.S.A.
Age 15

Let My Cries Be Heard

Can someone help me?
Is anyone there?
Can my cries be heard
Over your despair?
I need some help,
Don't you see?
You're supposed to be
Watching out for me.
My tears are here,
My eyes are red
And all you can do
is give me a pat on the head.
Can't you listen?
Don't you care?
I'm balling my eyes out,
Do I even dare?
I see you sad,
I see you cry,
Do you mind me
Asking you why?
Do you have a reason
for being sad?

(cont.)

I bet they're not as good
As some that I've had.
Can someone help me,
Is anyone there?
Let my cries be heard
Over your despair.

Amanda Frazer, Ohio, U.S.A.
Age 15

Seeing My Inner Self

It glistens when the sun hits it
And makes light shapes on my walls.
They only stay for a little bit.
Bad luck for years if it falls.

It tells me "wash your face,"
Or "do your hair."
Sometimes I stand there only in one place
And can't help but only stare.

It tells me if I'm only plain,
Or if I'm a little cutie.
But I can't help but only complain,
Because it will never show my inner beauty.

Kristina Hardenbrook, Massachusetts, U.S.A.
Age 15

Hello Stranger

Did you ever wonder
While walking down the street
If you've ever met
The people you meet?

Hello, neighbor
Have we ever met?
Hello, stranger
It's good to see you again...

I know I haven't kept in touch
I'm sure I don't know you anymore
Let's meet again
This time I'll remember you for sure

Jennifer Ostwinkle, Iowa, U.S.A.
Age 16

Confusion

Behind the smiles
Behind my laughing
Behind my giggling
There's a secret no one knows
Hidden deep in the pits of my heart
Like the black,
midnight sky
My fear crowds my life
worry and fret
Of a long lost wish
Wanting only what I lost
And regretting what I gained
Lost in my evil desires
Reaching
Screaming
Longing for my past
Filling my pillow with tears
Soaking my mind
with love
and hate

(cont.)

Behind all the smiles
Behind all the laughing
Behind all the giggling
One can hide
The biggest secret of all
A secret so strong
and so fulfilling
A secret known to me as
Myself

Sarah Manson, Michigan, U.S.A.
Age 18

Clean Your Room

"Clean your room!"
My Mom's voice goes boom
As I head down the hall groaning
I hear the rest of my siblings moaning
I open the door and look around
And I can't even see the ground!
There are clothes, magazines, and ties for hair,
Books, bags, and games strewn here and there.
My sister refuses to touch anything
After she sees the many things
Every second the piles seem to grow
Of stuffed animals, barbies, bookmarks, and Play-Doh™
Boxes and happy meal toys
Legos and doll house pieces, these are not great joys.
With a frown on my face while I clean the room
The floor is finally clean enough to vacuum.
With things finally straight and neat,
My Mom yells "bed time!" So I say "What?
I didn't even eat!"

Kim Lentz, Virginia, U.S.A.
Age 14

Once I was afraid, once I was scared
thought nobody heard me, nobody cared.
Even if they did listen, they wouldn't understand
my life was a game where I lost every hand.
Even in this city, where people push by
I felt so alone, where nobody heard my cries.
I wanted strength, I wanted peace
all I wanted, was for my heart to be at ease.
Then one night, as I was heading for bed
a small voice whispered inside my head.
"Don't be troubled, its not to late
its right in your heart, behind a locked gate.
Only you have the power, you have the key
turn that lock and set yourself free.
Love who you are, and who you are not
understand the world, and live a lot."
I took the advice, and turned the key
and to my surprise I could finally see
the curtains had fallen, and there was light.
What a wonderful discovery, an amazing sight.
Here was a world so different and so new.
The grass was so green, the sky was so blue.
Once I was afraid, once I was scared
but now I heard me, and I cared.

Kat Lai, Indiana, U.S.A.
Age 18

Limitations

Could I? Yes.
Should I? Yes.
Will I? ...No.
Their laughs & bitter, crude remarks,
Their bony fingers pointing —
Their heartless, cold, & rigid souls
Mocking.
Their tasteless words, their careless actions;
For so much I could do & say
Were it not for the sour aftertaste inflicted by my peers.
Was I set here on earth to please my fellow people?
Shall you command & shall I follow?
My friend, I warn thee...
Fate has its ways,
Life takes its tolls.
Just be careful in what you do & say —
Do you see that lost, forgotten child over there?
That could be you one day.

Skye Schader, Michigan, U.S.A.
Age 15

Heart

If there were any justice, I'd have a normal heart.
I would be able to run, or have the simple pleasure
of climbing a flight of stairs.
I could go anywhere, do anything, and not worry about
oxygen, altitude or anything
If there were any justice I wouldn't need medication.
Pills, liquids they all taste the same.
I could go to school and not panic,
if I forgot to take my "meds"
The liquids taste awful, the pills are hard to swallow,
and their side effects are dangerous also.
If there were any justice I wouldn't need this chair.
I would weigh a little more, and be sick a little less.
I could go to school all day, and be my very best.
But if there were any justice, I wouldn't be myself.
The people know me for who I am, not anybody else.
So I guess in a way, you don't need any justice,
Just as long as you are YOURSELF.

Ryan Moore, Texas, U.S.A.
Age 16

She Hides Behind Herself

She paints her face with makeup
Covering her soul.
Dyes her hair all colors
So she can play her role.
With diamonds in her ears
And a perm in her blonde hair,
She wears her platform shoes
In hopes people will stare.
She giggles with her girlfriends,
Talks with boyfriends on the phone.
Kinda makes you wonder
What she's like when she's alone.
I think there is more to her
Than her silly flirting games.
She must want something deeper
Than her lists of boyfriend names.
Does she wonder who she is
As she looks into the mirror?
Perhaps that she will find out
Is her greatest fear.

Edith Hoag-Godsey, Michigan, U.S.A.
Age 15

Never Again

Alone today but not tomorrow,
Tomorrow I'll be fine but today I feel sorrow,
I'll be out tomorrow free at last,
I'll try not to ever think of the past.
What will I do? What will I be?
My options are slim cause I've committed a felony.
I was just a kid but still frightened to this day.
That's right, I took someone's life away,
I do not believe they are letting me out,
I will no longer have to kick, scream and shout.
I will never think of committing another crime,
Crossing a red light or stealing a dime.
Will God ever forgive and forget,
These are questions,
and the answers I do not know yet.

Jeff Shornick, New Jersey, U.S.A.
Age 16

My Life

From my bedroom window I can see a field,
Sometimes if I look hard enough, I can imagine myself
standing there on an autumn morning.
Just standing there thinking and letting the early,
morning mist roll over my body.
The complete silence is a sweet release from all the
problems of life.
Through my mind a thought passes.
No matter what happens there will always be a fresh
page to start on tomorrow.
But what do people do when they run out of paper?
Some hide or just ignore the problems...but not me.
Life is special if you have friends to encourage you.
There is always hope no matter how bad you feel.
I stand there thinking. Waiting. Listening.
All I hear are the pine trees swaying in the gentle wind.
I am fine. I'll be okay.
As I stand there in my silent solitude,
an unexpected smile arrives upon my face.
I am lucky to have great friends. I am lucky.
A joy filled tear drips down my cheek.
I return to the window once again
and leave for school.

Steve Perkins, Ontario, Canada
Age 15

Not Ready

I don't think I'm ready
For what you have in mind.
You said we'd be friends first
And that we'd take our time.
Just because they do it
Doesn't mean I will too.
I will when I feel ready
But now I'm still confused.
I don't know how you feel
But I know I'm scared.
If your love is real
Then promise you'll be there!

Melissa Arocho, Florida, U.S.A.
Age 17

Beauty

I walk home in the starlight
anything is possible,
and I own the world.
My feet are bare.
Wild flowers are woven through my loose braids
and my hair tangled by the wind.
My brother's shirt protects my heart.
Jeans fit like they should.
Sunglasses perched on my head,
catch moon beam kisses.
My well worn uniform of laughter, childhood, and
eternal innocence.
I hum quietly to myself
as I wish on the star farthest away.
I stop walking to play with the ring on my thumb,
twisting it back and forth,
pausing to hear the breeze dance with the wind chimes.
The sparkles in my nail polish
mirror the ones in my eyes.
I breathe in the sweet night air
and I know,
I am beautiful.
For a rare moment I know who I am.

Kari Moore, Georgia, U.S.A.
Age 17

Smile

Smile! Don't you know everybody's watchin'?
You gotta look happy,
even if you aren't.
You gotta look pretty,
even if you're feelin' ugly.
You gotta act smart,
even if you don't know all the answers.
Don't let 'em know
when they've let you down.
You won't ever be disappointed
if you never expect anything.
Save your tears
for when they really matter,
or else they won't mean nearly as much.
Don't let anyone see
that you ever feel anything.
Just smile and be
the person everbody else
wants to see,
even if it's the last person
you want to be.

Rachel Sherwin, California, U.S.A.
Age 16

Acceptance

Whatever life holds,
I'm not quite sure I'm ready,
but I'll roll with the punches
and go with the flow.
I'll learn to accept
and make the best of
whatever cards I'm dealt
because accepting is sometimes
a greater strength
than being ready.

Rachel Sherwin, California, U.S.A.
Age 16

Heartache

Yesterday,
It was all so clear.
Right was there and left was here.
But something has happened
And I don't know where I am.
The poets always say
Be true to your heart.
But how can I?
When my heart gives me
an impossible choice.
I want to be cruel
I want to be cold
But something has seeped inside me
And I can't ignore your voice
echoing in my mind.
Time and distance are logical reasons
to be apart.
But when has logic mattered
When it comes to my heart?

Julia Wotton, Seoul, South Korea
Age 17

Mirror Images

When I look into the mirror
I see a girl who often sheds a tear.
I see her eyes so big and brown,
a familiar face that holds a frown.
Her nose so little and so square,
her lips so thin and so bare.
I look at her face and see her hell
She's been through a lot, as anyone could tell.
Can't anyone help this poor girl out,
by showing her what life's all about?

Jessica Tibbit, Indiana, U.S.A.
Age 19

Raped

You rape me, again, with your eyes.
I shall understand the incomprehensible
to belong to you
and become a figment of your imagination.

I am incapable
of overcoming
my hate of life and
the overpowering guilt of my sin.

My body is not my own
any longer.
You robbed me of my dignity.
You said it was something unquenchable.

My mind is drifting into oblivion
From here
All goes black
The abstraction is all my own.

(cont.)

Irreversible thoughts of suicide
consume me
and words aren't enough
to heal the scars already imprinted on my skin.
I have lost myself to you.
Every shred of me
that is left
becomes one with you

And dies.

Jen Amos, Ontario, Canada
Age 17

The Pond of Life

Reaching out to touch the water
  to hold the dream
    and caress the future.
My hand breaks the surface
  and shatters the glass
    of a life I could not have.
Cupping my hands together
  I try to pick up the love
    and own the faith.
But my hands begin to shake
  and I watch the joy
    slip through my fingers.
Putting my mouth to the water
  I try to drink the happiness
    and swallow the pleasure.
But my dry lips soak up the water
  and my tongue stays hot
    with all of the hatred.
Finally I plunge my head into the water
  to take a deep breath
    and watch life elude me,
Like the water that fills my lungs.

Jamie Lynn Houston, Nebraska, U.S.A.
Age 17

In Too Deep

Grab my hand, love
I'm sinking fast.
Pulling me in, love
The more I struggle to be free.

Grab my hand, love
I'm in over my head.
Dig me out, love
For I can no longer breathe.

Wave good-bye, love
I have disappeared.
Do cry for me, love
I'm in too deep.

Velma Danielle Segars, South Carolina, U.S.A.
Age 20

Chapter 2:

Family

Poem to My Mom

There is a place within my wish
for a little girl to grow,
Inside the head of a loving mom
where she'll learn all she needs to know.
And for a time she is content,
there's lots of room to play,
She's warm and sheltered, always safe,
but here she cannot stay.
The wish is far from what can be,
for nothing stays the same,
But what she'd give for simpler things,
if life were such a game.
For a place where she could disappear
inside a tight embrace,
And never have to feel a tear
fall down her saddened face.
And for some time this place is real,
perhaps the time goes fast,
The ticking clock starts keeping time
and memories do drift past.
For in this wish inside this head
the space gets cramped and small,
The little girl is reaching out,
beginning to get tall.

(cont.)

The hand that touches the head within,
where the child seems to be,
Has got to one day release its grip
and set the child free.
The clock that sits upon the wall
will tick its loudest yet,
Things that were ignored before,
much harder they will get.
One night when she's let out to play,
you see, too late you'll learn,
There comes a time that is the last
and she will not return.
The wish can never come quite true
but the little girl is strong,
But inside a head she can't grow up,
it's not where she'd belong.
She needs a chance to laugh and hurt,
make sense of things she does,
Begin to grow up by herself
and build on who she was.
At times she'll want to shut her eyes
and make things go away,
Crawl back inside the head she left
and there she'd always stay.

(cont.)

The clock that let the minutes go,
she'll think of with a sigh,
Of the tickling, dancing, laughing times,
the precious stage gone by.
The wish where life begins its path
holds purpose through it all,
But the head where the child begins to grow,
will one day get too small.
And the little girl will venture out
on her pathway that is set,
There's love and laughter and heartfelt words,
and a place she'll never forget.

Alison Dankmeyer, Ontario, Canada
Age 18

Too Late

There we were
Yelling and screaming
Shouting false insults
Both of us steaming.

I'd had enough
Of these fights
So I got up and left
I didn't care what was right.

I walked on out
Without saying goodbye
As Mother stood
Wiping a tear from her eye.

I told her then
I'd never come back
Of course then
It was wisdom I lacked.

Years went by
And I mean what I say
I never called her
Not to this day.

(cont.)

Very deep down
I felt some regret
But I was stubborn
Not one to relent.

'Til one morning I answered
My ringing phone
When I was feeling
Especially alone.

And a sobbing voice
Rang in my head
"It's all over,
Your mother is dead."

I refused to forgive
And look at my fate
I learned this lesson
But now it's too late

Amanda Rahn, Michigan, U.S.A.
Age 14

Imagine a ...

Imagine a telephone
It's sitting on a brown nightstand,
which happens to rock
(one leg is shorter than the other)
It's sitting on a floor,
which is covered with a deep blue shag carpet
"Deep Blue" that's what it said on the sales tag
It smells like the perfume she spilled on it.

Imagine a mother
Sitting by the phone
waiting for her child to call,
to tell her she is okay.
As the mother sits by the phone
she falls asleep on the blue shag carpet.
There is nothing particular
that stands out about this mom,
Brown hair, medium height,
small tortoise shell glasses
Sometimes too giving
but nothing that particularly stands out
about this Mother.

(cont.)

Imagine a police officer
picking up the phone.
His forehead begins to pound,
his heart skips several beats
and his lungs scream for more air.
He is a rookie,
This will be his first call of this nature.
The other officers pity him,
It's the most dreaded call
an officer can make —
calling a mother to tell her that her child,
her eternal baby,
her constant source of loving anxiety,
won't be coming home tonight.

Jasmyn Blueford, Maryland, U.S.A.
Age 16

Lost

I'm lost
I don't know what to do,
My map is gone
And my compass too.
I'm so sad
I can't help but cry,
You laugh at me
I turn away and sigh.
I can't see you
Or any sign,
But you say
It'll be just fine.
I close my eyes
Squeeze them tight,
And what do you know
You were right.
The sun is shining
The grass is green,
And I feel good
In fact pretty keen.
Thank you Daddy
I miss you so,
But you're still here
That I know.

Erin Wetovich, Florida, U.S.A.
Age 14
Featured in the February 1999 Poetry Contest

Chapter 3:

Spirituality

Eternal Life

When your time comes,
You will know
That it's when God needs you,
So you will go.

Find the light,
It's up so high,
Over the mountains,
In the sky.

Up in the clouds,
God will wait,
Until you come,
To open the gate.

When He does,
Walk inside,
For you have found the light,
The light that leads to eternal life.

Crystal Gayle Armendarez, Texas, U.S.A.
Age 15
Featured in the July 1999 Poetry Contest

Angel For Me

God sent me an angel
from heaven above,
to take away my sorrow
and fill me with love.
He sent my angel
to calm my fears,
to hold me close
and dry my tears.
My angel is always
there for me,
Whether deaf to hear
or blind to see.
He gave me a gift
so precious and true,
He taught me that love
never had to be blue.
God sent me an angel
for one precious day,
My angel taught me a lot
But just couldn't stay.

Amber Riegel, Illinois, U.S.A.
Age 15
Winner of the February 1999 Poetry Contest

I Need to Reach My Heavenly Father

I need to reach my heavenly Father,
Do you know the number to his phone?
I need to reach my Heavenly Father,
So I know that I am not all alone.
I need to reach my Heavenly Father,
See his face in front of mine,
I need to reach my Heavenly Father,
So that I can learn about him and not be left behind.
I need to reach my Heavenly Father,
Hear his voice loud and clear,
I need to reach my Heavenly Father,
I need his love, I need him here.
I need to know my Heavenly Father,
So I can go home with him one day,
I need to talk to my Heavenly Father,
I want to know all he has to say.
I need to hug my Heavenly Father,
So I can remember his soft touch,
I need to reach my Heavenly Father,
I need him to know, I love him so much.

Andrea Helen Stewart, Idaho, U.S.A.
Age 16
Featured in the June 1999 Poetry Contest

Angel

A hope,
a dream,
water flowing down the stream.
An act of faith,
a confession,
be safe in her protection.
A plea for mercy,
a hopeful grace,
wipe the tears from your face.
A desire,
desire to be free,
like the calm waters flowing in the sea.
Don't be alone,
don't let your life pass you by,
for a beautiful love cares for you
and she comes from the sky.

Charity Sutton, California, U.S.A.
Age 14
Featured in the July 1999 Poetry Contest

Night Lights

Twinkle, sprinkle, dusty gold,
What messages do the stars hold?
Are they the eyes of the unknown,
Or people surrounding our Father's throne.

Are stars the spirits of the dead,
Or just an image all in our head?
Could they be tiny candles burning bright,
Or lights to show our way on a dark night.

Is a shooting star an airplane
Or wings that an Angel was about to gain?
Maybe it's a ship landing on Mars,
Or maybe the reflection of the lights of our cars.

Look in the sky on a clear silent night
And examine each and every light.
Let your mind wander away
And listen to what the stars have to say.

No matter what science has to say,
The magic of a star can be looked at in every way.
The real meaning will never be told,
What message does your star hold?

Chelsey Ellis, New Brunswick, Canada
Age 15

Emotion

I've been through the clouds of hopelessness,
Walked through the fields of hate,
Seen the jungles of fury,
Swam in oceans of fate.
Ran in rolling fields of grief,
Passed by the mountains of tears,
Heard the screams of agony,
Deep within the forest of fears.
Tasted the grit of death in my mouth,
Played a game of deceit,
Seen a raging river of lies,
Felt anger's scorching heat.
So much bleakness in the world,
But none compared to above,
All the emotion in this world,
Couldn't stand up to God's love!

Amanda M. Dungan, Missouri, U.S.A.
Age 17

You

Your voice instilled in me a ray of hope,
Your eyes let me hold my head up high.
Your touch commanded me to live,
Your lips, they taste like wine.
I always wondered how it'd be,
To have someone just for me.
Mama always said you were so kind,
But I never paid her any mind.
Yet now I know just what she meant,
For I have received the gift you sent.
I never meant to cause you pain,
But I knew I was to gain.
You took me under your sheltered wing,
You taught me how to really sing.
I thank you, Lord Almighty, for all of your blessings.

Tania Irizarry, Texas, U.S.A.
Age 16

Chapter 4:

Colors and Nature

The Chance of a Flower

Think of all the petals of all the flowers ever sent,
Did you ever stop to wonder who received them,
where they went?
The sentimental feelings
and the comfort that they bring,
Or the times that lack forgiveness
when this gift won't mean a thing.
The daisy that is innocent that holds a message tight,
A moment that can ease distrust
make all things seem all right.
A flower that can spark a smile or provoke a tear to fall,
Each flower holds a promise deep within its petal wall.
But when the feeling leaves the room,
and love has gone away,
The precious bud that blooms for now
may only last the day.
Think of all the vanities, that poor misguided rose,
A flower speaks in silent words the heart already knows.
Love cannot be counted on for love is blind at best,
And love will break your heart in two,
a flower's final test.
For when the petals wilt and fall,
regret and grief are shared,
But tears dry up and memories fade
with the flower's beauty spared.
And love is usually restless and a flower dies in shade,

(cont.)

But a blossom sent with good intent
is like a promise made.
'I'm sorry' or 'I'm here for you',
'I thought of you today',
Each flower says 'I love you'
in its own unique, small way.
But a heart will one day cease to beat
as the flower falls apart,
And pain will one day touch your life
as love will touch your heart.
And tears will try to soothe the wounds
they cannot seem to fix,
And a flower tries to shield the eyes
from love's relentless tricks.
And inside every flower's seed
there lies the softest smile,
With hopes the flower opens up
and love will stay a while.
We all get fooled by feelings
and perhaps we trust too fast,
But your eyes just see a flower
and your mind forgets the past.
When you decide to take a chance,
on love you'll risk it all,
May you receive this special gift
and petals to soften your fall.

Alison Dankmeyer, Ontario, Canada
Age 18

My Blue

Blue is the ocean
Blue are your eyes
Blue is the bluebird
Blue are the skies.

Blue can be cold
But my blue is warm
Blue makes me happy
Not sad and forlorn.

Blue is the sparkle
That brightens up my day
I wish I was blue
In every way.

Blue is the water
Blue is the sea
Blue is for you
But my blue's for me.

Kathleen Anne McMahon, Victoria, Australia
Age 14
Featured in the April 1999 Poetry Contest

Sunshine

Streams of gold
Here and there
Flowing 'round everywhere
As the golden ball
Sets in the sky
Cotton balls
Float nearby
Up above that great oak tree
It sits and waits for you and me
Shining down with morning glee!

Danielle Konopka, Connecticut, U.S.A.
Age 13

Orange Arrogance

If orange is for arrogance,
then red must be for love;
blue must be for misery
and gray must mean a dove.

Yellow must mean sunshine
and innocent speaks of pearl;
pink must curtain a baby's room,
if the doctor claims a girl.

Yet how many colors surround us here
and how many meanings have they?
Could orange not stand for confidence
and life the red portray?

Blue may stand for sweetness,
gray could signify flight,
yellow might become gaiety
and pearl transform to light.

Pretty pink, as the saying goes,
might blaze up into fire,
and colors, shy to reveal themselves,
into the pattern they would retire.

(cont.)

Into the most measured pattern,
where every line is straight,
where colors mean the same each day,
in a world of pre-destined fate.

If we could only rip the seams,
and break the folds unbroken,
maybe meanings would surprise us all,
and color the dreams we've chosen.

May all your gray mornings hide yellow and red,
may all your pearl nights turn to pink,
still you'll let your dreams soar out into the blue,
while to earth orange arrogance does sink.

Lauren Connelly, Maryland, U.S.A.
Age 16
Featured in the June 1999 Poetry Contest

Not one word
can ever describe
the wonderful feeling
of standing right there
just in the middle
of a beautifully pouring
thunder storm
and looking up at the sky
having the droplets
gush down my face
smearing my make-up everywhere
running down my clothing
that is now clinging to me
warm against cold
and watching the lightning
play tag across the sky
while the thunder is yelling
in my ear
and I jump
to splash the puddles
seeing how far
the water goes
as I am
dancing and dancing
through the rain.

Andrea Barclay, Ontario, Canada
Age 16

Sunset

All the different colors as far as the eye can see,
seem to be floating gently, staring back at me.
The blues and the purples, the pinks and the greens,
all come together with nothing in between.
The blues are getting darker, the colors they cascade,
the pinks are getting distant, the greens have turned to gray.
The grays are now black, the stars shine bright,
the moon engulfs me in pale moonlight.
The sun tips the mountain, my colors I see,
my sunset is now staring back at me.

Alisha Perdue, California, U.S.A.
Age 15

As the Sun Goes Down

As the sun goes down, the light fades away,
And with it the world falls into its dreams.
When the sun goes down, it is the end of day,
And its water flows in rivers and streams.

Darkness spreads 'round like a thundering cloud,
As lightning strikes its core.
The sounds are great and the shattering is loud,
Then the world stops and says, "no more."

Night continues on, yet day seems so far,
Not knowing if light will ever return.
So the world waits, gazing at a star,
Hoping that there is an end to the darkness' burn.

As the sun goes down, time stands still,
And the world ponders without mind.
Wait for the day? Yes the world will,
Hoping that light is what it will find.

Christopher J. Deano, Illinois, U.S.A.
Age 18

Goddess Garden

Magic clouds with magic powers
Raining little magic showers,
Planting little magic flowers
In the garden of the goddess.

Where trees can stand 100 feet tall
And fairies dance by the waterfall,
You can hear the echo of a bird's call
In the garden of the goddess.

In the morn, the garden is shaded by trees
So you can feel the soft cool breeze,
The midnight beauty brings you to your knees
In the garden of the goddess.

Exotic flowers, sweet fruit, blue water, and fresh air,
You'll live in the garden without a care.
Her spirit, you'll know is always there,
In the garden of the goddess.

Jennifer Eileen Cobb, Illinois, U.S.A.
Age 13

Chapter 5:

Friends

A.K.A. Friend

One to confide in,
There 'til the end,
Shares my deep secrets,
A.K.A. friend.

Lifts up my spirits,
My heart she can mend,
Wipes away tear drops,
A.K.A. friend.

She smiles when I'm happy,
But a shoulder she'll lend,
Whenever I'm lonely
A.K.A. friend.

Helps fight my battles,
She's here to defend,
If she's here I'll be safe,
A.K.A. friend.

Jessica Cox, Pennsylvania, U.S.A.
Age 16
Featured in the March 1999 Poetry Contest

Popularity

They expect you to be pretty,
They expect you to be thin.
They expect you to be someone cool,
Someone who can fit in.

They expect you to be someone you're not,
someone you're not going to be happy with,
A whole new different personality,
Or is this whole thing just a myth?

They expect you to do the things they do,
like the drugs and the alcohol,
But if you refuse to go with it,
Then you're not one of them at all.

They never really were your friends
The true blue ones you hear about.
They're as easy as you would imagine they are,
To not come running when you shout.

Sure they are the popular ones,
but in the end it's true,
Those pretty, perfect people need to see,
They are the same as me and you.

Aarti Talwar, Ontario, Canada
Age 14
Featured in the June 1999 Poetry Contest

Friends

You say that you are my friend,
Or so that is what I like to hear,
But when I needed someone to talk to,
You were never there.
I listened to your problems and helped you
as much as I could,
But now you listen to what others say,
A lot more than you should.
One day you are my friend
and the next you are talking about me.
I hope that this will make you realize
and help to make you see.
If I am wrong, I apologize
And all of my love I send,
But if I am here just for you to talk about,
Then I am sorry, but you are not a true friend.

Michele Booths, Pennsylvania, U.S.A.
Age 15

A Friend's Prayer

Here's a prayer my friend,
That I pray for you.
And I hope that God answers it,
I truly do.

God I know you're listening
So I'll ask you one thing
Please help out my friend
And let her heart sing.

Watch over her God
Help her see the light
Please protect her Lord
Through days as dark as night.

Thank you for listening
I pray you will send
An angel to protect her
Thank you and Amen.

Elizabeth Gray, Texas, U.S.A.
Age 14
Featured in the April 1999 Poetry Contest

Friends

A desert storms ceases.
Everyone gathers up their pieces.
Something may end but never be lost.
Pain can not be sold at any cost.

Pain is not present, it's in the past.
It's not something to forget, it will always last.
People whom we love will leave.
People who said they cared, will deceive.

Everything that was supposed to last,
Will disappear, all too fast.
Nothing will stay, it all will change.
Yet our friendship will never be out of range.

Friends may not last forever, true.
Yet if pain does, then so shall you.
If pain can last, happiness will prevail.
And in the end, this friendship will sail.

People may die, but souls never truly part.
Maybe not side by side as friends,
But always in heart.

Amanda Granger, New York, U.S.A.
Age 15
Featured in the February 1999 Poetry Contest

Angel Without Wings

You stand there with bravery,
A courage so strong,
And I know in my heart,
I cannot be wrong.

You're an angel in disguise,
Without its wings,
You showed up in my life one day,
Providing everything.

Giving me knowledge,
And showing you care,
And when you leave my side,
I still feel you there.

Your presence warms my heart,
And I wish I could give you everything,
You are my best friend,
My angel without wings!

Colleen Broms, Oklahoma, U.S.A.
Age 14
Featured in the May 1999 Poetry Contest

Forever

Tobacco, alcohol, cocaine, and crack.
These things you do behind my back.
I love you dearly, I love you so,
But these things will have to go.
If not for me, then for yourself.
I wish you'd see that you need help!
These chemicals can ruin dreams,
don't you realize what that means?
I wish you'd see, I wish you knew,
I wish there was something else I could do.
I'll try my hardest, I'll try my best,
to stop you from taking your final rest,
FOREVER!

Lianne E. Graf, Pennsylvania, U.S.A.
Age 16

What Happened?

Do you remember
When nothing really mattered?
When we played with everyone,
No matter if boy or girl?
What happened?
Now, this thing called love
Gets in the way
And everything's a bit more complicated.
But, no matter what happens,
Now, or in 20 years,
I will forever be here!
Just answer me one question,
What happened?

Matthew Glennon, Virginia, U.S.A.
Age 15
Dedicated to Nicole A. of New Hampshire

My One True Best Friend

I don't think I tell you enough
that you are the very best
even through the rough times
you stuck around unlike the rest.

Even though you're gone now
I wish you could see
you'll never be replaced
and you'll always be with me.

Nobody could ever fill that space
that space you have in my heart
and nobody could ever tear
our best friend bond apart.

We're inseparable apart
and irresistible together
that's why you'll be
my best friend forever.

(cont.)

Whenever I needed you
you were always there
to comfort or to listen
so I know you did care

What I'm trying to say
is that I hope this friendship doesn't end
because you're always and forever
my one true best friend.

Jessica Paredes, Texas, U.S.A.
Age 15

What Friends Are Made Of

What friends are made of is special,
This you should cherish,
When you are with your friends you can tell,
This friendship will not vanish.

Friends are made of kindness,
When you need a helping hand,
Your friend is where you'll find,
Someone who'll understand.

A sacred thing is friendship,
It doesn't have a price,
True friendship is kindred souls,
And rarely happens twice.

Sara Diane Allison, Texas, U.S.A.
Age 14

Chapter 6:

Love Found

Distant Love

How can you say you love me,
When you've never seen my face?
You've never touched my hair,
Or seen me cry.
We've never walked along the beach,
Hand in hand, as the sun set.
We only know each other
Through a virtual world.
We're virtual strangers.
But beneath it all,
There's this peculiar connection,
That binds us beyond all reason and logic,
And I've never been more scared.
How can I let you go?
Just when I'm starting to love you, too.

Julia Wotton, Seoul, South Korea
Age 16

I Don't Want to Say Goodnight

Your arms embrace me
and hold me tight.
I look into your eyes
longing for a kiss goodnight.

Your soft lips meet mine
and our hearts intertwine.
Still holding me tight,
I don't want to say goodnight.

As you pull away
I hold you against me.
I wish you would stay,
please don't leave me.

Part of you remains with me,
together we will always be.
I long for your soft lips
pressed against mine.
When once more our hearts
will intertwine.

Hold me forever outside my door.
I will miss you until we're together once more.

Rebecca Lynn Wilson, Pennsylvania, U.S.A.
Age 16
Featured in the February 1999 Poetry Contest

Beautiful Angel of Mine

Your beauty is enchanted,
Your love is like a fire.
Your voice is like the Heaven's angels
Singing in a choir.

The moon shines and makes a glow
Upon your delicate skin.
Your loveliness is bringing out
My emotions deep within.

I look at you, you look at me,
Our lips slightly touch.
And then I kiss your rosy cheeks,
And say I love you very much.

We walk along the moonlit beach
Without knowing what the night will bring.
Then I kneel down beside you,
Ask you to marry me, and give you the diamond ring.

Oh you must be an Angel,
So beautiful and kind.
Words could never tell how much I love you.
Beautiful angel of mine.

Heath Lyle LeBoeuf, Florida, U.S.A.
Age 14
Featured in the July 1999 Poetry Contest

Love

A feeling of weightlessness,
Floating through the air,
Not a care in the world,
Total happiness with life,
Is it fate or accident?
Does it really matter?
A friend and companion,
To trust in forever,
Love, the greatest feeling.

Andrea N. Shannon, Florida, U.S.A.
Age 13
Featured in the October 1998 Poetry Contest

Light Feet, Red Roses

Early this morning, someone came,
"Your Secret Admirer" they signed as their name.
Walking with light feet
Quiet as a mouse,
He left the roses at my house.
Redder than red,
Fresher than morning dew,
He ended the short letter with "I Love You."
I saw you leaving,
I know it was you,
At that very moment, my love for thee grew.
Let's both tell the truth about how we feel,
The love between us, I know is real.

Jennifer Eileen Cobb, Illinois, U.S.A.
Age 13

Him

He walks amidst the stars of night,
He beams a bright celestial light.
To set my lonely heart aflame,
At just the mention of his name.
Helplessly I float away,
I'm swept along confusion bay.
I'm drifting past the shore of chance,
Where happy hearts together dance.
A whirlpool of forbidden thought,
Where love's strong current has been caught.
I smash upon the rocks of doubt,
Defenseless I am tossed about.
Thrown into a sea of tears,
Rocked by violent waves of fears.
My boat is broken by the tide,
My longing passions all subside.
I'm emptied in a pool of calm,
To watch the waters sweep my qualms.
And on the bank in angel's light,
His smile illuminates the night.

Chelsea Rhinebarger, Ohio, U.S.A.
Age 16

Chapter 7:

Love Lost

It's in the Past

The love we've shared
The things no one knew
For each other we cared
Inside ourselves we grew.

I've finally realized something
something everyone else has
The thing we had now is nothing
And I need to understand it's in the past.

Everyone thought we were cute together
But only a few knew
That we couldn't get along together
It wasn't because of me or you.

It was because we never connected
But tried very hard to,
And although all both of us were affected
Apart is how we grew.

So it took me a long time to realize
But it dawned on me at last,
Whenever I go, whatever you do
Whatever we had is in the past.

Sarah Gourdine, South Carolina, U.S.A.
Age 16
Featured in the February 1999 Contest

Not Supposed to Be

I know we're only friends.
That's how it's supposed to be.
But I get this funny feeling,
Whenever you're not with me.
When you're out with other girls,
And I'm here all alone,
I start wishing you were here,
And stay up wishing you would phone.
I'm not supposed to feel like this.
It's not supposed to be.
I'm not supposed to dream we'll kiss,
Or hope that you'll want me.

If I told you how I feel,
Would you see me differently?
Would it change your mind at all,
In how you look at me?
Is it strange for me to think,
That we might ever be?
Or should I forget my feelings,
And live in this misery?
I'm not supposed to feel like this.
It's not supposed to be.
I'm not supposed to dream we'll kiss,
Or hope that you'll want me.

(cont.)

Life is so complicated,
Changing from day to day.
But like the sands of time,
My love is here to stay.

Courtney Miller, Ontario, Canada

Standing Alone

I remember a time
quite long ago,
As I write your name
here in the snow,
When I was here
and you were, too.
Now I am here,
but where are you?
That was a time
long, long ago,
I stand now alone,
in the freezing snow.
I look at the sky
that now seems stark,
And now my heart
feels very dark.
I remember the kisses
that promised you'd stay,
Yet why am I standing
alone here today?
I remember the touches
how good they once felt,
I wish I could tell you
how you made my heart melt.

Cory Fauhl, Montana, U.S.A.
Age 16

Who Are You?

I feel like I don't even know you.
The double face? The double world?
The double heart?

I see your face, smiling and warm,
The same as the day before.
But who am I kidding?
I don't know you.

I see your world, the one I'm part of,
We see each other and have a good time.
What's going on after I leave?
I don't know you.

I feel your heart, open and fragile
What you have given to me, I treasure
Who else has the same access?
I don't know you.

I found your life so confusing and torn.
You just listened to what I'd say,
never sharing a single word.
I have never heard what's behind that face,
or what's racking in your brain.
Then reality hits and I face the music,
Who am I kidding?
I don't know you.

Heather Robinson, Kansas, U.S.A.
Age 18

The Chance

The air is cold,
the sun sets
and I feel the raindrops falling
on my crowded head.
The wind blows
and I feel your memory
brush past my lips
boldly,
almost bitterly
then it's gone
and I cry,
silently to myself
because I want nothing more
than the chance
to fall in love with you.

Davette JoAnne Cooper, Minnesota, U.S.A.
Age 17

Today

When I see you walking by
I take a look, dream, then sigh.
And when I sit and think of you
I know my love is very true.

I wish that I could say
What's always on my mind
But when I think I can
I get chills sent down my spine.

I am falling for you harder
Than I ever thought I would
So I am going to tell you now
What I've always known I should.

I love you very much
Ever since the day,
I saw that smile upon your face
And let it steal my heart away.

Janessa Pons, New York, U.S.A.
Age 16
Featured in the April 1999 Poetry Contest

A Place in My Heart

There is a place within my heart
Where memories of you lie,
A place I visit from time to time
A place that shall never die.
A place that no one knows about
Except for a very few,
A place that I have set aside
Especially for you.
I go to this place whenever I feel
Lonely when we're apart,
I go to this place whenever I need
You to touch my heart.
You shall always be there
And I will be there, too,
No one else could take your place
For I give my heart to you.

Joel Sievers, Victoria, Australia
Age 16
Winner of the July 1999 Poetry Contest

Absence of You

I can see the sky
and beyond
I can see the ocean
and beyond
I can see into your eyes
and beyond
But when I look at the ocean
it is brown
And when I look at the sky
it is white
And when I look into your eyes
They are blank
I am in the absence of blue
I am in the absence of you.

Kate Bluhm, California, U.S.A.
Age 15

Thoughts of a Madman

A translucent orb of fire,
searing shut the pain,
My eye reflects the sorrow
and closes with disdain.
Her shadow narrows gradually,
her footsteps slowly fade,
As she walks away I realize
it's my heart and soul that paid.

All I wanted was a reason
and excuse to let her go,
Yet she haunts me with her image
causing pain you cannot know.
Everything I gave to her,
all my wishes, thoughts, and fears,
Meant nothing to her heart
as she leaves my eyes in tears.

(cont.)

My lips tremble for a moment
though the words do not appear,
How I long to call her back,
to make her stand and hear.
All the reasons she should stay
and what she meant to me,
If only she could care again,
if only she could see.

Even now my heart sinks deeper,
though her shadow is no more,
I tell myself it's over
as my knees fall to the floor.
I'm not sure when I'll stand again,
I think only of the pain,
When the drug of love betrayed me,
it made me go insane.

John Lee Hagan, Ohio, U.S.A.
Age 16
Featured in the February 1999 Poetry Contest

Will You Be Mine?

The time has come
the wait is over,
I've searched for you
my whole life over.
No more waiting
or anticipating,
every night and every day
in each and every little way.
I'll be yours,
will you be mine?

Michelle McCann, Texas, U.S.A.
Age 14

Eyes For Me

You talked about her so much, I didn't seem to mind,
Then I looked into your eyes to see what I might find.
But what I found was a love that wasn't for me,
The light is starting to shine, and now I begin to see.
With my heart of gold and my soul of fire,
I no longer see you as a man, I see you as a liar.
I lie in tears with a heart that's broken,
While you speak the words that shouldn't be spoken.
I should have seen it coming from a mile away,
I should have known it was my heart you'd betray.
I know now that I cannot change the past,
But everything seemed to happen so fast.
So I lock up my heart and throw away the key,
Because now I know you never had eyes for me.

Meghan Leff, California, U.S.A.
Age 17
Winner of the June 1999 Poetry Contest

I'm Not The One

I can tell by your eyes,
you love another.
I can tell by your voice,
I shouldn't bother.

If there's a chance,
I wish there was a sign.
My heart is there for you,
but you decline.

I wish I could take you out
to a wonderful place.
I'd hold your soft hands,
and kiss your angelic face.

But I'm not the one,
that's how it is.
So I wish for you,
A life full of bliss.

Scott Yoshimura, California, U.S.A.
Age 17

I Did But You Didn't

I spoke
But you didn't listen.
I changed
But you didn't notice.
I walked away
But you stood there.
I tried
But you made no effort.
I turned left
But you turned right.

Now you're speaking
But I'm not listening.

Kate Glass, Pennsylvania, U.S.A.
Featured in the February 1999 Poetry Contest

All I Can't Say

There's so much I can't say
when I look into your eyes.
I'm worried you'll reject me
and hurt my foolish pride.
Each day this love grows stronger
but I could never let you know.
There's so much behind my smile
that I could never show.
I'd hold you for a lifetime
if you would only let me in.
I'd love you like no other
but you just don't understand.
Every time I'm with you
I never want us to be apart,
But you only reject me
and break my fragile heart.
So I'll dream of us together
of just how good it could be,
And all my love for you
will remain a silent part of me.

Tiffany Roane, Montana, U.S.A.
Age 17
Featured in the July Poetry Contest

Was It Love?

Love, what is it?
Love, can you describe it?
Was it love?

I thought I found someone
I thought she might like it
I was wrong...But
Was it love?

I'm not sure yet
If it was
It didn't last long
So again I ask,
Was it love?

That is the question
What is the answer?
I wish I knew
But to find out
I think I have to wait

So I finally ask,
Was it love?

Brian Jones, Vermont, U.S.A.
Age 15

Tell Me Again

If it's over and we're really through,
If there's nothing else that I can do,
If you're playing a game that I can't win,
If you don't love me, then tell me again.

Tell me again as you walk out the door,
That you don't love me anymore.
Tell me how we can just be friends,
I'm not sure I heard you, so tell me again.

I pick up the phone and hear your voice,
It's all I can do to barely breathe.
I know that you said goodbye,
But tell me again before you leave.

One day my heart will mend,
But if you ever loved me, please tell me again.

Courtney Nixon, Tennessee, U.S.A.
Age 17

Missing A Piece

Living another day
trying a little less,
learning how to let go of you,
remembering how to forget.
Taking another breath,
dwelling in the past,
staring at images in my head,
wanting to make them last.
Making another move,
another I'll regret,
slipping away from consciousness,
losing self respect.
I owe it all to you
who tied a ball and chain to my heart,
you stripped me of my happiness
and left me in the dark.
I'm picking up the pieces,
looking for the glue,
something to hold my life together,
the only piece missing is you.

Rachel Rene Frost, Ohio, U.S.A.
Age 15

Love for an Angel

Sight to see
An angel sleep.
My heart doth ache.
Mine eyes do weep.

And hearing, I hear
An angel's voice
Yet ever hearing
Is not a choice.

To live without.
To always want.
The mem'ry is torture.
Heart's ghost does haunt.

Eternal dawn.
Paradise past.
'Twas the first time.
And will be the last.

To love that angel
Love not returned.
Dreams are shattered.
Hopes now burned.

(cont.)

The answer is simple.
"Love not," you say?
"Ne'er," I'll reply.
"There is no way."

No chance is there.
No joy is nigh.
Helpless to change.
Worthless am I.

No answers to see.
None time will show.
Love tortures me still.
There is nowhere to go.

So now you know truth.
The reason I cry
The love for an angel
Yet still, you ask, "Why?"

That blessing and torture.
That angel, so sweet.
Time, let love be returned
Or let me forever sleep.

Matthew Graham, Louisiana, U.S.A.
Age 17

Chapter 8:

Our World

Nice Guys Finish First

They called him dork or spaz or geek,
"Let's make fun of him and peek,
At his A+ quiz that we shall fail,
Cuz we're big and we prevail!"
See, Edmund was the king of smart,
Him and a book never part,
Glasses, braces, suspenders, too.
We all poked fun, yes even you,
But what you just didn't realize,
Was he was above all us guys.
While we flirted and passed our notes,
He took them in pen protected coats.
Little did we know but he,
We would one day in Fortune see.
You were stealing Ed's lunch when last you met,
Now you fix him lunch in his penthouse suite.
The jock who hit him, stole his seat,
Now drives Ed's limo down the street.
So don't pick on Ed,
Or any geek,
Cuz he'll rule your world,
And you'll be meek.

Lauren Blaire Friedman, South Carolina, U.S.A.
Age 14
Featured in the May 1999 Poetry

Perfection?

You tell us to be sexy,
But not sexual.
You tell us looks are only skin deep,
But if we're different we're ugly.
You tell us to be ourselves,
But we should dress this way.
You tell us to be smart,
But not smarter than boys.
You say we should be proud of the way we look,
But you invented plastic surgery.
You say imperfection is beautiful,
But we should wear make-up.
You say size doesn't matter,
But we would be better as a size two.
You say beauty is in the eyes of the beholder,
But looks are as far as the eye can see.

Angela Brothers, Nova Scotia, Canada
Age 17

Rose

A splendid rose stood,
all alone.
Surrounded by a wall
of stone.
Around the wall were
roses, too.
Still neither knew the
other grew.
So often we, like flowers
dwell
Too deep within our
human shell.
And pass through life
not understood.
Nor making all the friends
we should.

Christi Bergschneider, Arkansas, U.S.A.
Age 17

Love Conquers All

When you look up at the sky,
Do you ever stop and wonder why
We were put upon this earth,
And what was the meaning of our birth.
Is there a god or is it just fate,
That we live in this world of hate?
Is there any supreme power
That makes it snow or makes it shower?
Should we bow before his might,
Or should we take up arms and fight
Against the so-called Mighty One?
Or is it that we've already won?
The freedom to do what we please,
The freedom to get off our knees.
And not have to bow before
The creator of this world of war.
But no matter how often you fall,
In the end Love Conquers All.

(cont.)

You should live the way you choose,
By doing that you'll never lose.
So when life gives you a choice,
Just listen to your inner voice,
And it will lead you the right way,
And never let you go astray.
So here's the message I give to you,
Remember this in whatever you do:
No matter how often you fall,
In the end Love Conquers All.
When your back's against the wall,
Just remember that Love Conquers All.

Michael Marchand, Texas, U.S.A.
Age 15

Rumors

Softly dropped, the words we hear
Around the grapevine
Of yesteryear.
Secrets told without a thought,
Words that we have not forgot.
No regard for wrong or right.

False or true, words hold us tight,
Blinding until we can't see,
Blurring our reality.

Spoken poisons change our minds
Leaving common sense behind.
Malice makes our hearts
Grow weak,
From the day when first we speak.

Sheena Kroeger, Kansas, U.S.A.
Age 16

Don't

Don't cry if you feel scared or even all alone.
Don't cry if you think the world around you
went cold and turned to stone.
Don't shed one tear if the love of your life
has found another girl.
Don't get upset if you get lost
in this big and confusing world.
Don't get angry with the people
who treat others so unfair.
Just make sure that for those "others"
you'll stand up and you'll be there.
Don't pity yourself if someone deliberately
tries to bring you down.
Just think of how special you are
and turn the situation around.
The reason why I say these things
you should and shouldn't do,
Is because these are very mature matters
average teenagers go through.

Kaelyn Feeney, Pennsylvania, U.S.A.

Times Change

Times change,
And people get older.
The sun fades,
And this world gets colder.

Friends part,
And enemies unite.
We wander through life
Never knowing what's right.

When push comes to shove
And things get rough,
Never give up,
Stand tall and be tough.

Knowing that one day
It all will be gone,
Enjoy what you have,
For it may not last long.

Renee Garin, Pennsylvania, U.S.A.
Age 16

Stop the Violence

A shot pierced out
The world crashed down
Nothing was the same
After that deadly sound.

The night was dark
The air was cold
Nothing was right
As the story is told.

Why did it happen?
Does anyone care?
Is the world too violent?
Go outside...do you dare?

The young life was not forgotten
For at the funeral many came
Another victim of violence
Are you the one to blame?

Steph Swieter, Iowa, U.S.A.
Age 15

Children

The children, they play
In their own little places,
It's a magical wonder
To see smiles on their faces.
Not a worry they have
About how life will be,
How they talk and laugh
Their thoughts worry free.

Prancing around, little girls in their dresses,
Happy and dirty little boys and their messes.

Each to his own
And his own to each,
A lesson to learn
These children will teach.

The older we get
The more worry will show,
How happy we were
We may never know.

(cont.)

Learn from the younger
Experience from the old,
Leave adult thoughts
to freeze in the cold.
And remember childhood memories
To cherish and hold.

Casey Pierce, New York, U.S.A.
Age 17

Wanting To Be Free

A girl is sitting alone in class,
Pretending not to hear the words that pass.
Words of disgust, of hate and disdain,
Directed at her time and again.

A beautiful bird that cannot fly,
Broken heart, broken wings, nothing but cries.
Wanting ever so much just to fly free,
Instead it is here, and here it will be.

The girl is walking home from school,
Once again today she was made the fool.
She looks at the bird and can only cry,
For she sees her pain mirrored in its eyes.

Samantha Sarrels, Illinois, U.S.A.
Age 17

Life's Challenge

Life is a garden
Full of hidden enchanting secrets.
Graceful flowers, shining with beauty,
Everywhere I gaze.

They delicately sway with the wind
So vulnerable to change and neglect,
They provoke many a question.
In that way, life is a maze.

Wherever you turn there are walls;
Walls of bewilderment, walls of fear,
Walls that you may overcome,
But never understand those whom you hold dear.

Like a maze, life is a challenge,
One that you may accept or deny.
Life only comes once.
Step up and give it a try.

Linda Swart, Georgia, U.S.A.
Age 15

Respect

To give respect to one another,
Is to care for them like a sister or brother.
It is to show someone that you really care,
To compromise, outlook, and always be fair.
To be respectful you shall show dignity,
Also speak nothing but honesty.
You could be respectful to just about anyone,
A teacher, parent, or even a friend in a marathon.
To be respectful is to show forgiveness,
And not to laugh at someone's weakness.
Give a compliment or two to make someone feel wanted,
It will make them feel special, unique or gifted.
To give respect to someone else,
You have to learn to respect yourself.
To show respectfulness you have to learn,
To give everyone a chance or a turn.
Everyone has the right to be respected,
A friend, a crossing guard or a guy running to be elected.
So don't forget to respect all,
Whether it's spring, summer, winter, or fall.

Mishal Hashmi, California, U.S.A.
Age 14
Featured in the February 1999 Poetry Contest

Where Have The Children Gone

Too young for drugs.
Too young for sex.
Too young to love.
Why do children
put themselves into pain?
What happened to childhood games
and friends being on the brain?
The power, the hate
that young ones now feel.
What happened to praying
at night as they kneel?
Babies having babies,
Children killing cops.
What happened to the day of candy
and sweet lollypops?
The children are gone.
No youth to spread.
Now thoughts of rape
lurk through her head.
The boy down the street
with a son as old as my brother,
The child next door
who was killed by her mother.

(cont.)

We can pray
and we can cry,
But children all get older
and then die.
The children have grown,
they grew up too fast,
Not sweet like the little ones
who grew in the past.
Are these the times
the Devil has been longing for?
Will it ever be safe
for you to open the door?
Drive-by shootings
going on everyday,
Children spending time
on guns instead of play.
The boys who spent the afternoon
shooting up the school,
The girl who shot up heroin
just to be cool.
The girl who's time of the month
was two times too late,
The boy who carved in his own skin
a message of hate.

(cont.)

The children are sleeping,
the graves have been made,
In the small coffins
the children are laid.
Will all hopes of the future
fade away?
Or will it one day be safe
for my children to play?

Emily Pieper, Iowa, U.S.A.
Age 13
Featured in the June 1999 Poetry Contest

Empty Stomach

You look so fragile
Crumpled into a ball
Under the overpass;
A cement block for your pillow
And a piece of cardboard
as your blanket.
Oh, I'm so sorry,
I didn't mean to wake you
from your dreams of better times.
Do you mind
If I ask how you got here?
Where's your family?
Where's your home?
Oh, I'm so sorry
I didn't mean to make you cry.
Let me wipe the tear
From your soiled cheek.
Come, Sir,
Let me take you
To get something to eat;
To wipe the hunger
From your empty stomach.
And you can tell me
Of your past dreams.

Kristin Haynes, Texas, U.S.A.
Age 15

What If...

What if the sky was green and the grass was blue?
If you were me and I was you,
If we grew young instead of old,
If we could say instead of being told,
If we ruled the world and normal was strange,
If youth was treated equal, would anything change?

Heatherliynn McDonald, British Columbia, Canada
Age 16

Chapter 9:

In

Remembrance

Daddy's Gone

I walked in the room
and the people just stared.
They came up to me
and they told me they cared.

I sat in the chair
below his feet,
then I looked at his face
and my heart skipped a beat.

I knew he was gone
but I refused to believe,
that my daddy had died
and had left me to grieve.

So I walked by his bed
and his body I shook,
I thought he'd wake up
and that my pain would be took.

But his body just laid there
so stiff and so cold,
he'd no longer be there,
for our family to hold.

(cont.)

Then I ran to my room
and continued to cry,
when the hearse pulled up
I wanted to die.

Then they took him away
and I felt all alone,
my daddy has died
and he's not coming home.

Heather West, Ohio, U.S.A.
Age 15
Winner, April 1999 Poetry Contest

Reality Check

On the 20th of April,
Something shook our state.
There was a shooting in a school,
A crime done out of hate.

When we heard about the tragedy,
Our hearts filled up with tears.
Though we feel bad for all those dead,
Crying just hides our fears.

The truth is we were scared
Because we could have been the ones to die,
And deep inside we were happy for ourselves
Even though we cried.

Some may think it selfish,
But we're human and we do care.
We try to understand,
And help without being there.

(cont.)

We pray for the friends who will always remember,
And the families who can never forget,
No matter how many cards we write
Or how many candles we've lit.

But when the angels cried on the rainy morning
That the doves were released to the sky,
The clouds revealed the sunshine
And their souls were free to fly.

Charlotte Alvarado, Colorado, U.S.A.
Age 16

Baby Boy

Sweet small child
Shy little smile
A temper so mild
Baby once mine.

Shining blond hair
Bright blue eyes
Showed not a care
Baby once mine.

Warm in bed
Little hands grasp Teddy
Rest little head
Baby once mine.

Hardly a tear
Sweet dreams are near
Baby once mine.

(cont.)

Growing day by day
Something went wrong
Sleep seemed to stay
Baby once mine.

Kneeling each night
Hope growing dim
Nothing seems right
Baby once mine.

Head laid to rest
Eyes finally close
Peace found at last
Baby now yours.

Jill Huwe, Minnesota, U.S.A.
Age 16
Featured in the March 1999 Poetry Contest

I Love You Too

As I sit on the bed
I kiss my father on the head.
I hold his hand and begin to pray
that God will take his pain away.
I tell him everything is alright
(which I plainly know is a lie)
I tell that I love him as I begin to cry.
He tells me he loves me too
As he wipes the tears from my eyes.
He tells me not to cry,
everyone has to die.
This is it, this is his time,
Everything is gonna be just fine.
I beg him not to leave,
With his last breath he says to me,
"I Love You."
I look at him and realize he is dead.
There is nothing more I could have done or said.
I sit there crying and shaking.
Why did God have to take him?
I'll always remember his last words.
"I Love You."
I whisper to myself, "Dad I Love You, too."

Brittany Lynn Hanauer, Indiana, U.S.A.
Age 15

My mom was my best friend,
She said she would be there to the end.
But I can't sit here and lie,
The hardest thing I ever did is say goodbye.
We would hang out as if she was my sis,
Now the fights are what I miss.
I remember that sad day,
The doctor said she couldn't stay.
The helpless look in her eyes,
And her last words, "I'll miss you guys."
It's enough to make us all stop and say,
"Why do people just go away?"

Tara Nicole, Alabama, U.S.A.
Age 14
Winner, July 1999 Life Poetry Contest

Through an Angel's Eyes

I was Sissy.
Nothing bad could ever happen to her
When I was there,
But I wasn't around.
Now she's lying in a hospital bed,
Tubes running in
And nurses running out.
Her lips are cold,
I'll never get to
Put lipstick on them again.
Her feet are freezing,
They'll never wake me up
When she runs into my room
In the middle of the night
because she's scared.
Her body is stiff,
I'll never be able to hold her again.
I can't kiss this away.

*This is dedicated to my little sister, Skye, who died in the
summer of 1997 when she was 2.*

Kristin Haynes, Texas, U.S.A.
Age 15

Your Presence Will Never End

I really want to see you
And smile with you again.
But you're too far for me to reach,
Too far away.
I sometimes hear old songs
And think of you and cry
Remembering how sad it was
Saying goodbye.
You're in a better world now
At least better than this place,
Cause here it seems like we're always
Running an endless race.
The worst thing was you died
Such a painful death,
I wish I was by your side
To witness your last breath.
But though your eyes I can't see
I know you're here watching over me.
I'm thankful to the Lord
For blessing me with you as a friend.
And I know although you're gone
Your presence will never end.

Hannah McDowell, Auckland, New Zealand
Age 15

Sadly Happy

I still miss you
Remember that I always will
But time is wearing my memory of you
And memories of you
Have started to fade
Much to my chagrin
I thought you'd stay in my mind forever
But I was so young when you died
And now I know I was wrong
I still miss you - but I can't remember you
I closed my eyes and tried to dream
Of your soft and tender embrace
But I woke up empty handed
Without ever recalling your touch.

Jenni Ostwinkle, Iowa, U.S.A.
Age 16

I Do Not Sleep

Do not stand at my grave and weep,
I am not there, I do not sleep.
I've gone to the heavens high above,
And wrapped myself in godly love.
There the angels gave me wings,
And I listened as one angel sings.
I look around for people I know,
They had died a long time ago.
I was a bit scared when the time came to die,
But let me say there is no time to cry.
So live your life as I've lived mine,
You can not turn back the hands of time.
God has given you the gift of life and love,
Until the day comes that brings the white dove.
The white dove will bring you all the way here,
So do not cry, have no fear.

Blair Meeks, Florida, U.S.A.
Age 14